Ponty an' Pop

GREN of the South Wales Echo

The start of the season is always an exciting time as optimistic plans are made...

HERE WE GO AGAIN. ANOTHER BRAND NEW RUGBY SEASON STRETCHES AHEAD OF US, AND NO WHERE IS THERE A GREATER SENSE OF EXPECTANT EXCITEMENT THAN AT BEAUTIFUL ROYAL ABERFLYARFF (a mecca for culture lovers) WHERE THE FORTHCOMING SEASON IS VIEWED WITH GREAT OPTIMISM.

LOOKS **PROMISIN'** DUNNIT?

COULD BE THE **BIG ONE** FOR ABERFLYARFF!

RICK WRIGHT MAY BUY WRU. ECHO.

WORKED HARD THIS CLOSE SEASON WE HAVE - TO GET THE GROUND BROUGHT UP TO **WRU BASIC**!

NOT (GASP) **FLATTENED** IT OUT!

OH NO, JUST FILLED IN **MOST** OF THEM MINE SHAFTS.

IT'LL TAKE A BIT OF THE EXCITEMENT OUT OF THE HOME GAMES BUT THE WRU CAN BE **FUNNY** ABOUT THINGS LIKE OPEN MINE SHAFTS.

WRU LOTTERY: **NEXT MONTH** WIN IEUAN EVANS IN A **VOLVO**!

GREN · 13-8-96.

Ponty - is Mr Aberflyarff RFC, he's the club chairman, the secretary and he is also responsible for team selection and sending reports of the team's latest game to the local press.
An ex-Aberflyarff player who would give his life for the club (unless he had a better offer from Cardiff). He and **Pop** are co-authors of 'Aberflyarff RFC - The Glory Years'.

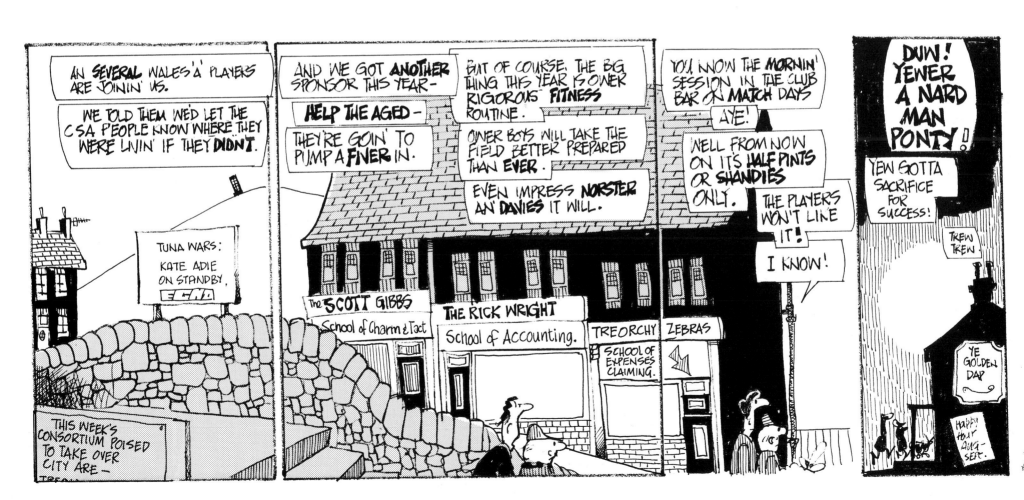

of the South Wales Echo

Will Royal Aberflyarff RFC ever become really comfortable in this new professional world of rugby union?

EACH DAY WE READ ABOUT THE STAGGERING EARNINGS OF RUGBY PLAYERS IN OTHER PARTS OF THE WORLD.
SO WHEN THE SPORTS ECHO (the Trumpet of Truth) GETS TO THE HIGHER REACHES OF SCRUMCAP VALLEY, READERS IN LOVELY UNSPOILT ROYAL ABERFLYARFF TOO, ARE AMAZED AT SUCH STORIES

ACCORDIN' TO THIS WRU BLOKE EVEN **WELSH** PLAYERS 'AVE BEEN GETTIN' PAID.

NEVER! I **CAN'T** BELIEVE THAT.

'OUR PLAYERS WERE PAID' - WRU
SHOCK HORROR EDITION
SPORTS ECHO

NOR ME TO NEITHER.

I CAN'T BELIEVE WELSH PLAYERS **EVER** GOT PAID.

MIND YEW, 'AVE YEW READ THIS ABOUT NOT SOME *SOUTHERN HEMI-SPHERE* PLAYERS GET PAID?

SOME ARE GETTIN' £50,000 SIGNIN' ON FEES. THEN A **BASIC** OF £60,000 A SEASON.

ON TOP OF THAT THEY GET A JOB WORTH £70,000 WITH THE SPONSOR.

CON CLUB
PUB
RUGBY CLUB
BAR
LABOUR CLUB
OFF LICENCE

L' TISS TO LIVE IN CWM?

* SOUTH OF NEWPORT.

SUNDAY SERMON WHY IT'S NO LONGER A SIN TO GET PAID FOR PLAYING

Gren · 9.9.95.

Ponty an' Pop

GREN of the South Wales Echo

Most clubs now boast a 'youth policy'. So too at Royal Aberflyarff..

ROYAL ABERFLYARFF RFC ARE JUSTIFIABLY PROUD OF THEIR YOUTH POLICY. YOUNG LADS, SOME DIRECT FROM THE MATERNITY WING ARE FED INTO THE CLUB SYSTEM WHICH ENCOURAGES TALENT AND TEACHES TECHNIQUE.
THIS SYSTEM HAS MADE ROYAL ABERFLYARFF (Motto - He who dares should wait until the refs not looking) THE HOT BED OF PROGRESSIVE RUGBY, AS YET ANOTHER TEENAGER FORCES HIMSELF INTO THE FIRSTS.

GOOD HEAVENS IT'S LITTLE IANTO THUNDERTHIGHS INNIT?

YES SIR I'M THE LATEST PRODUCT OF THE CLUBS BATTERY FARMING FOR YOUTH RUGBY.

I SAID 'NO' TO ZEBRAS.

'YOU THUNDERTHIGHS' HAVE BEEN PLAYIN' FOR ROYAL ABERFLYARFF FOR GENERATIONS.

YEW GOTTA LOT TO LIVE UP TO SON.

TELL ME MORE ABOUT THEM. WHAT BLOOD DO I HAVE COURSIN' THROUGH MY VEINS?

I CAN REMEMBER THUNDERTHIGHS PLAYIN' GOIN' BACK TO YEWER GREAT GRANDPARENTS DAY AYE.

WELL, LIKE YEW-A PROP; BUT HUGE, NASTY AN' 'ORRIBLE.

DONOR EGGS FOR SALE £5 DOZ

ME ♥ WRU

DON'T TELL ILLINGWORTH ABOUT TONY COTTEY-HE'S FOR TOO GOOD FOR ENGLAND

GREN 27.8.94

It's the annual problem. Who will be the club captain for the forthcoming season?

ONCE AGAIN IT'S THAT TIME OF YEAR WHEN SERIOUS CONSIDERATION IS BEING GIVEN TO WHO WILL HAVE THE HONOUR OF BEING CAPTAIN FOR THE SEASON.

SO, TOO, AT TROPICAL ROYAL ABERFLYARFF WHERE SUCH CAPTAIN RESPONSIBILITIES ARE NOT OFFERED LIGHTLY.

WELL **WHO'S** IT GONNA BE THEN?

THE WORLD (AND WELSH SELECTORS) WAIT FOR NEWS OF NEW ROYAL ABERFLYARFF CAPTAIN.

CARLING BEGS FOR JOB BUT NOT CONSIDERED

'SNOT **EASY** ISSIT?

YEW CAN'T GIVE IT TO JUST **ANY-ONE**.

NO WE'RE LOOKING FOR A NATURAL **LEADER OF MEN**.

SOMEONE WHOSE ON-FIELD DECISIONS WILL BE **INSTANTLY** ACCEPTED AND **ACTED** UPON.

SOME ONE WHO CAN **LEAD** BY EXAMPLE.

A PLAYER WHO'S **DONE** IT ALL, **SEEN** IT ALL.

UP BY THERE   DOWN BY HERE

GLAM TO PIONEER HALF DAY CRICKET RUMOUR DENIED

Pop is now full-time unemployed, he lost his job at Aberflyarff's Japanese factory when hi-tech came in - he wasn't replaced by a computer, he was replaced by a pocket calculator.

SOMEONE WHO OTHER PLAYERS WILL **DIE** FOR.

SOMEONE WHO COMMANDS INSTANT **RESPECT** BY **ALL** WHO MEET HIM.

THAT'S THE WAY I LIKE IT ????

A MAN WHO REPRESENTS THE CLUB WITH QUIET **DIGNITY**.

ONE WHO'S NOT **TOO** FRIENDLY YET NOT **TOO** STAND OFFISH **!**

SOMEONE WHO CAN MAKE FINE SPEECHES.

SOMEONE WHO REALLY **CARES** ABOUT THE GAME, THE FANS **AND** THE WRU.

WOOF. WOOF.

GLAMORGAN

GLAMORGAN MORGAN

AH WELL - THAT'S **EVERYONE** IN OUR CLUB OUT OF IT **!**

OH, JOYO!

9

Ponty an' Pop

GREN

GREN
of the South Wales Echo

The new season brings with it a new excitement as so many things are planned for Welsh Rugby

THERE IS AN AIR OF EXCITED ANTICIPATION OVER LOVELY ROYAL ABERFLYARFF AS THE RUGBY CLUB PREPARES ITSELF FOR THE NEW SEASON. EVERYONE IS SURE IT'S GOING TO BE A SEASON TO REMEMBER.

SO **MANY** THINGS TO GET EXCITED ABOUT EH **?**

HELLO-O

AYE, THERE'S OWER NEW **OVERSEAS** PLAYER. I CAN'T UNDERSTAND A **WORD** HE SAYS BUT HE SEEMS QUITE **NICE**.

HE'S NOT OWER OVERSEAS PLAYER MUN - HE'S FROM **LLANELLI.**

AND OF COURSE WE'RE **CONFIDENTLY** EXPECTING TO BE INVITED TO PLAY IN THIS NEW **EUROPE** LEAGUE.

EUROPE ??? THAT'S **ABROAD** INNIT **?**

AYE, NEAR **BENIDORM** I THINK **!**

AND, OF COURSE THAT NEW **SPORTS** COUNCIL GRANT ADDED TO THE **COUNCIL** IMPROVEMENT GRANT, AND THE MONEY FROM **CADW** AND THE **WRU...**

MATT FINISH DECORATOR

ED DIBBLE · PIE SHOP ·

MINNIE STRONEY · ITALIAN RESTAURANT.

10

The papers are full of drug taking within sport. Will this habit spread to Royal Aberflyarff RFC?

Like all top clubs Royal Aberflyarff RFC needs sponsorship to survive...

AS SINFUL PROFESSIONALISM EXPLODES IN RUGBY, IT'S BECOMING INCREASINGLY OBVIOUS THAT ONLY CLUBS BACKED BY HUGE SPONSORSHIP DEALS CAN COMPETE AT TOP LEVEL.

SO AT LOVELY NUCLEAR FREE ROYAL ABERFLYARFF WHERE THE CREAM OF OUR TALENT IS BEING PLUNDERED BY RICH CLUBS, AGAIN THE QUESTION OF ATTRACTING SPONSORS IS TOP PRIORITY.

AN' A FIRM MAKIN' THEM SURGICAL TRUSSES.

AN' HORLICS.

THAT'S NOT THE SORT OF IMAGE WE WANT FOR THE CLUB.

I GOTTA SEE A POSSIBLE SPONSOR TODAY. ISSA BREWERY!

THAT'S THE SORT OF IMAGE MORE IN KEEPIN' WITH OWER ATHLETES.

LOOK WHAT HAPPENED THE LAST TIME WE LOOKED FOR SPONSORS.

ONLY THREE OFFERS.

A FIRM MAKIN' GRAVE-STONES.

BIG CHEST FOR SALE RING LIL

HAVE BOOTS -WILL TRAVEL SCRUM HALF TEL

INTELLIGENT HOOKER - CHEAP TO A GOOD HOME -

WAIP FOR SALE

£300 WEEK REAL DIRTY BLINSIDE

RUGBY LEAGUE REJECT SEEKS CLUB-BARGAIN

FRENCH LESSONS

HOUSE TRAINED PROP £100 PER INK

A N·OTHER WILL GO NORTH NO OFFER REFUSED

EX-WELSH CAP SEEKS NEW HOME £300 PER GAME

MUST MOVE CLUB DESPERATE! ANY CLUB WILL DO —EXCEPT SENGHENYDD.

MILLENIUM FUND MAY BUY CITY A STRIKER SPORTS · ECHO

COME BACK TAFSCOTT!

ANY CARDIFF MEMBER NOT PREPARED TO VOTE FOR MOVE TO BAY WILL BE SHOT. REPORT DENIED — READ SPORTS ECHO STORY

MUST CHANGE CLUB ANY THING CONSIDERED —EVEN ABERCWMBOI

NICK LEESON TO SPONSOR CAERPHILLY?

ECHO

GREN '95

Bromide Lil - darling barmaid of the Golden Dap. Still a part-time sex symbol and model for welding gloves and pit boots. She and Ponty were once engaged - this was broken off as soon as she had the ring valued. Lil will do almost anything for a North stand ticket.

THERE'S THIS TOP MAN AT ONE OF OWER BIG BREWERIES, CALLED **OWEN ARWYN** - HE'S SEEN US PLAY - AN HE WANTS TO SEE ME ABOUT A **SPONSORSHIP** DEAL.

PROBE INTO BEDWAS RFC...

THANK YOU FOR SEEIN' ME MR ARWYN.

REALLY... OH, TA ... THANK YEW.

PONTYPRIDD

HB

BASS

WHADEE SAY WHADEE SAY?

WELL HE'S SEEN US **PLAY** A FEW TIMES. AN' SEEN THE SET UP WOT WE GOT YER AT THE **CLUB**.

AN' YES THEY **ARE** PREPARED TO PUT **MUNNEY** INTO OWER CLUB!

HOW CAN THEY AFFORD PROP PETER JONES...

QUESTIONS MAY BE RAISED AT WRU. Honest.

AS MR ARWYN SAID. HE FELT THEIR OFFER WOULD **REFLECT** IN WOT HE THOUGHT THE NAME OF ABERFLYARFF WOULD BE WORTH LONG-TERM TO HIS **BREWERY**.

YE GOLDEN DAP.

A PUB WITH A DIFFERENCE - IT'S NOT AN IRISH THEME PUB

PLEASE DO NOT DROWN HERE AT LOW WATER

GREAT, AN DID YOU SIGN UP A SPONSORSHIP THERE AN' THEN?

AN HAVE THE MUNNEY?

NO I DIDN'T HAVE CHANGE OF HIS TENNER

SAD REALLY INNIT

Ponty an' Pop

GREN *of the South Wales Echo*

Royal Aberflyarff RFC like every other club it seems want to sign Jonathan Davies when he leaves Warrington.

16

Ponty an' Pop

GREN of the South Wales Echo

It's time once more to follow our glorious team to Ireland for the Five nations game...

Ponty an' Pop

GREN

GREN
of the South Wales Echo

Once again members of Royal Aberflyarff make the biennial pilgrimage to Dublin for the Irish game.

PONTY, POP AND THE ROYAL ABERFLYARFF BOYS ARE DELIGHTED TO BE ONCE AGAIN IN DUBLIN FOR THE GAME.

AFTER A LONG JOURNEY IN THEIR FIFTY SIX SEATER COACH THEY ARRIVE AT THEIR HOTEL.

GREAT TO BE HERE AGAIN INNIT.

OH AYE, THESE PADDYS GIVE US A LUVLEY WELCOME THEY DO.

EVERY OTHER YEAR INNIT— THE SAME FIFTY SIX OF US IN THE SAME HOTEL.

WE BEEN COMIN' HERE FOR YEARS.

GREN . 2.3.96

D'YOU KNOW SOME PEOPLE DON'T KNOW HOW WE MANAGE TO AFFORD IT.

MIND YEW—THE DSS SUPPLYIN' THE COACH DOES HELP.

AN' THE FERRY— ACCEPTIN' IDWAL'S BUS PASS.

Nigel is the head groundsman at Aberflyarff's Sir Waldo Trahernia Sportsdome, a position he has held since giving up the game in 1980. He will always be remembered for that occasion in an Aberflyarff - England game when Will Carling, with no one to beat, the line at his mercy, twenty yards out, fell over him! And Aberflyarff went on to thrash England 3-Nil.

HERE WE ARE THEN - OWER HOTEL!

AYE, MUST BE **TWENTY** YEARS WE BEEN COMIN' HERE.

HELLO BOYS - **GREAT** TO SEE YOU AGAIN WELCOME TO IRELAND. BEGORRAH, BEGORRAH, BEGORRAH.

★★★★
The **STAMPING IRISH PROP**
A TRUSS HOUSE.

'OTEL

LUVLEY TO BE HERE PADDY LOOK YEW, ISN'T IT, YUKKY DAR, LIKE.

WELL HOW **MANY** OF YOU STAYING THIS YEAR?

SAME AS **ALWAYS**.

FIFTY SIX THEN IS IT?

YEP.

RIGHT! **TWO ROOMS** AGAIN THEN IS IT?

YES

SURE THATS **ENOUGH**.

Reception

AYE, THE DRIVER SAID HE'LL SLEEP ON THE BUS.

AN' THEY WONDER HOW WE AFFORD IT.

21

Ponty an' Pop

GREN

GREN of the South Wales Echo

Jonathan Davies plays his first game for Cardiff, and it did appear that the other fourteen players wouldn't pass the ball to him.

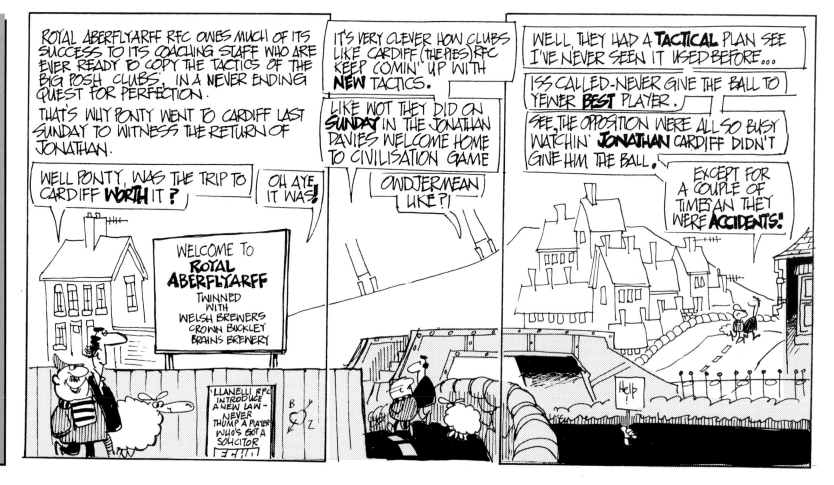

ROYAL ABERFLYARFF RFC OWES MUCH OF ITS SUCCESS TO ITS COACHING STAFF WHO ARE EVER READY TO COPY THE TACTICS OF THE BIG POSH CLUBS', IN A NEVER ENDING QUEST FOR PERFECTION.

THAT'S WHY PONTY WENT TO CARDIFF LAST SUNDAY TO WITNESS THE RETURN OF JONATHAN.

WELL PONTY, WAS THE TRIP TO CARDIFF **WORTH** IT?

OH AYE IT WAS!

WELCOME TO **ROYAL ABERFLYARFF** TWINNED WITH WELSH BREWERS CROWN BUCKLEY BRAINS BREWERY

'LLANELLI RFC INTRODUCE A NEW LAW — NEVER THUMP A PLAYER WHO'S GOT A SOLICITOR'

IT'S VERY CLEVER HOW CLUBS LIKE CARDIFF (THE PIES) RFC KEEP COMIN' UP WITH **NEW** TACTICS.

LIKE WOT THEY DID ON **SUNDAY** IN THE JONATHAN DAVIES WELCOME HOME TO CIVILISATION GAME

OWDJERMEAN LIKE?!

WELL, THEY HAD A **TACTICAL** PLAN SEE I'VE NEVER SEEN IT USED BEFORE...

ISS CALLED-NEVER GIVE THE BALL TO YEWER **BEST** PLAYER.

SEE, THE OPPOSITION WERE ALL SO BUSY WATCHIN' **JONATHAN** CARDIFF DIDN'T GIVE HIM THE BALL.

EXCEPT FOR A COUPLE OF TIMES AN THEY WERE **ACCIDENTS!**

Help!

23

of the South Wales Echo

Many lower division stars are being poached by rich top clubs. Could it happen at Royal Aberflyarff?

IT'S NOT EASY TRYING TO KEEP A LOWER DIVISION SIDE TOGETHER THESE DAYS, AS THEY ARE FINDING AT LOVELY ROYAL ABERFLYARFF (thought by many historians to be the site of Camelot) WHERE ITS SIDE, PACKED WITH LOCAL TALENT, IS ONCE MORE THE TARGET FOR FILTHY RICH CLUBS.

'SNOT FAIR ISSIT, CARDIFF 'AVE BEEN UP YER **AGAIN**, POACHIN' ONE OF OWER STARS — MADE AN OFFER THEY DID!

TYPICAL CARDIFF INNIT**!**

ALL CHEQUE BOOK AN' PIES.

WHO ARE THEY **PLUNDERIN'** THIS TIME **?**

OWER STAR NUMBER EIGHT — **ARNOLD NUTSTRAMPLER** BACK OF LINE OUT PROVOKER.

ARNOLD WON'T GO — BEEN AN' ABERFLYARFF MAN EVER SINCE HE **FIRST** LEARNED TO DEAD LEG.

JPR TO MAKE STATE VISIT OF PONTYPRIDD

ALL POLICE LEAVE CANCELLED

CENYDD THOMAS ON STAND-BY

'POP' ROLE EARNS OWEN MONEY BAFTA NOMINATION aye.

PONTY AND POP ON RADIO BBC WALES AT 6·05 FRIDAY. IN BACK PAGE

Ponty an' Pop

GREN
of the South Wales Echo

A bid for the new National Stadium to be built at Bridgend, not Cardiff has been announced...

THE RUGBY LOVING FOLK OF ROYAL ABERFLYARFF ARE VERY DISAPPOINTED THAT PLANS FOR THE WORLD'S GREATEST SUPERDROME AT CARDIFF FOR THE WRU HAVE HIT A SLIGHT SNAG. AND THEY ARE VERY MUCH AGAINST BUILDING THE NATIONAL STADIUM AT BRIDGEND.

ISS OWER BIRTHRIGHT INNIT! INTERNATIONAL RUGBY **GOTTA** BE PLAYED ON THE ARMS PARK!

TREW, TREW! ISS A VERY PROUD **HERITAGE** INNIT.

IF GOD HAD WANTED U,S TO PLAY RUGBY DOWN IN BRIDGEND HE **WOULDN'T** HAVE GIVEN US THE ARMS PARK.

THE ARMS PARK IS A MECCA TO PEOPLE ALL OVER THE **WORLD**.

THEY COME TO SEE THE **DEANS** DISPUTED TRY SPOT.

WHERE **GARETH** DIVED OVER IN THE MUD AGAINST SCOTLAND.

WHERE **ANDY HADEN** TOOK A DIVE...

WHERE THE **ALBERT FRANCIS** SUITE IS.

UPPER ABERFLYARFF TOP

UPPER ABERFLYARFF

YOU CAN'T HAVE MONEY SAYS THE MILLENNIUM FUND — NO SUPER-DROME

MOVE NAT STADIUM TO BRIDGEND SAY SOME MISGUIDED FANS

TWICKEN-HAM ARMS PARK

AD SPACE TO LET.

ROYAL ABERFLYARFF NEXT HOME GAME V MILLENNIUM COMMITTEE XV STAMP-OFF 3 PM

GREN · 14. 10 · 95

26

Arnold Nutstrampler - Still club captain after all these years, a player who is a fine example to all the up and coming youth thugs. Arnold still holds the WRU record for infringements in one game (104) and sendings off during one season (97). He has made the position of loosehead provoker his own since 1975. This is his benefit season, as long as they can get Owen Money and Dai Vaughan for the dinner.

Ponty an' Pop

GREN of the South Wales Echo

The names of applicants for the job of WRU coaching director have been leaked to the press.

AS ANY LOYAL READER OF THIS WONDERFUL NEWS-PAPER WILL KNOW, PONTY (the thinking man's Vernon Pugh) WILL NOT MISS AN OPPORTUNITY TO MAKE HIMSELF AVAILABLE TO RUN WELSH RUGBY. IT COMES AS NO SURPRISE THEREFORE TO LEARN HE HAS APPLIED TO SUCCEED ALEX EVANS.

'ELLO PONTY BOY. I YER AS 'OW YOU'VE APPLIED FOR ALEX EVANS WELSH JOB.

AYE, AS MUCH AS I ADMIRE 'IM — CONSIDERIN' HE'S AUSTRALIAN...

I FELT I OWED IT TO WALES TO APPLY FOR 'IS JOB.

AN' I HEAR AS YEW 'AD AN INTERVIEW TOO.

AYE, BUT I DIDN'T GET THE JOB LIKE!

WARA TEG INNIT. THEY WERE VERY NICE TO ME AT THE WRU THEY WERE ... ALMOST LIKE REAL PEOPLE THEY WAS.

THEY ASKED ME QUESTIONS — LIKE, WHY I THOUGHT I COULD DO THE JOB.

JONATHAN DAVIES JOINS CARDIFF

ABERFLYAREFF DIDN'T WANT ME SAYS STAR

CLUB RECORD

OPEN TO OFFER

ABERFH BID FOR BILLY BOSTON

ECH

TOM DAVID JOINS PONTY

Gren 4·11·95

28

Ponty an' Pop

GREN

GREN
of the South Wales Echo

Kevin Bowring is named as new Coaching Director.

RUGBY LOVERS AT ROYAL ABERFLYARFF (home now for many a media poseur) ARE DELIGHTED TO KNOW THAT AT LONG LAST (in fact at long, long last) THE WRU HAS ANNOUNCED THE NAME OF ITS NEW COACHING DIRECTOR. SO IT'S NATURAL THAT LIKE WELSH RUGBY FANS EVERYWHERE, THEY DECIDE IF THEY ARE GOING TO LIKE HIM OR NOT.

WELL KEVIN BOWRIN'S GOT THE JOB! WODJERTHINK?

I DON'T KNOW MUCH ABOUT HIM REALLY LIKE SEE.

WRU TO INTRODUCE GUESS YOURSELF A FIXTURE CUP.
WESTERN MAIL

KEV GETS WRU COACH JOB
Echo

I VOTED FOR BEBB'S SAYS WRU MAN
SPORTS ECHO

HAPPY BIRTHDAY HARRY POLOWAY

WELSH WOMAN OF THE YEAR - BROMIDE LIL JUST FAILS AGAIN.

DON' MATTER ABOUT THAT YEWER A WELSH FAN — ARE YEW GONNA LIKE 'IM OR NOT?

WELL, 'IM BEIN' WELSH IS GREAT IN MY BOOK.

I WAS WORRIED WE WAS GOIN' TO END UP WITH A FROG.

AN' ANOTHER THING IN 'ISS FAVOUR IS HE'S VERY INTELLIGENT.

OWDJERMAKE THAT OUT?

Attila Groinstomper is the club's open-side groiner. He has been watched by Welsh Selectors, Lions Selectors and Special Branch. This is Attila's tenth season at Aberflyarff where he is in hiding from the Child Support Agency.

WELL, HOW **OLD** IS HE **?** FORTY ONE **!**

AN' **STILL** IN COLLEGE INEE...

THERE'S A LOT OF LEARNIN' GONE IN THERE AFTER **ALL** THOSE YERS **!**

GREN'S GUIDE TO RUGBY NOMINATED FOR BOOKER PRIZE — GET YOURS BEFORE BOOKER BUYS THE LOT NOW!

ON SALE AT ALL GOOD BOOKSHOPS— AND A FEW DODGY ONES

YEWER RIGHT, AN' THAT'S WHAT WE **NEED** NOW IN THIS NEW AGE OF RUGBY... INTELLIGENT BLOKES **!**

YEW TAKE THIS NEW IDEA OF OUR OLD FRIEND HEINE KENS — THIS **EUROPEAN** LEAGUE.

SOPHIE RHYS-JONES WANTS TO HIDE FROM PUBLIC GAZE — SHE'LL BE AT EVERY GLAM WANDERERS HOME GAME THEN.

OWER BOYS ARE THE NEW BREED OF PLAYER

SHOOTIN' ALL OVER **EUROPE** TO PLAY.

AN' THAT'S WHERE **INTELLIGENT** PLAYERS WILL HAVE AN' **ADVANTAGE** EVERY TIME.

AYE, WHAT WE GOTTA DO IS PRODUCE **GOOD** PLAYERS...

WELCOME KEVIN BOY — NO OBLIGATION TO SELECT HERE.

THEM | US

HAVE | HAVE NOTS

HOME | AWAY.

WHO CAN VERBALLY ABUSE REFS AN' OPPOSITION IN **FIVE** EUROPEAN LANGUAGES AT LEAST **!**

THE FOUR BARS IN AT THE GOLDEN DAP

YE Gold Dap Inn

GREN 2.12.95.

31

Ponty an' Pop

GREN

of the South Wales Echo

The beginning of a new year is a time for optimism at most clubs.

32

GREN PONTY an' POP

It's BBC Wales Sports Personality of the Year time again...

YET ANOTHER BBC WELSH SPORTS PERSONALITY OF THE YEAR HAS BEEN ANNOUNCED AT A STAR SPANGLED OCCASION IN CARDIFF THIS WEEK.

ONCE AGAIN HOWEVER NOT A SINGLE ROYAL ABERFLYARFF PLAYER WAS EVEN CONSIDERED.

THEM BBC WALES BLOKES GOTTA **LOT** TO ANSWER FOR.

AYE THAT SORT OF THING COULD LEAVE A VERY **NASTY** PSYCOLOGICAL SCAR ON SOMEONE AS TENDERLY **IMPRESSIONABLE** AS 'IM!

ROYAL ABERFLYARFF POLY TECH **** THUG IN RESIDENCE ARNOLD NUTSTRAMPLER

HUGH JARCE GENTS TAILOR

MORT CHERRY FUNERAL DIRECTOR

HOME RULE FOR ELY.

AS WHO?

OWER ARNOLD NUTSTRAMPLER INNIT. HE MUS' BE **GUTTED.**

AYE AFTER THE **GREAT** 1995 WOT 'E 'AD.

TANYA SEX HAPPY HOUR 6-7

JUST WOT **MORE** COULD 'E 'AVE DONE TO GET THE SPORTS PERSONALITY OF 1995 AWARD.

LOOK WHAT HE'S DONE - SENT OFF TWENTY-FIVE TIMES IN 1995. -**STILL** A WRU ALL COMERS RECORD.

THEN THAT LITTLE DIFFERENCE OF OPINION HE HAD WITH EIGHT **NEATH** PLAYERS.

THEY'RE OPENING THAT BAR **AGAIN** SOON.

MAKES **VINNIE JONES** LOOK SHY AN' RETIRIN' HE DO.

BOTTOM SHOP VERY HAPPY HOUR 7-8.

OWEN MONEY SCHOOL OF GRACE & MOVEMENT

HUGO FARR TRAVEL AGENT.

PERSONALLY LIKE, I BLAME THAT ALAN WILKINS!

GREN 13·1·96

Erotica Jenkins is the club's physiotherapist, she specializes in groin strains. Her ambitions within the game are simple. If one day she meets someone who looks like Alan Wilkins with a couple of spare debentures her life will be complete.

AN ON ABOUT HIS CHARITY WORK — HE ORGANISED A TRIP TO EVERY BREWERY IN WALES, AN' EVERY SINGLE DISTILLERY IN SCOTLAND — **SPONSORED** LIKE.

AYE, OWER SECONDS WERE SPONSORED AS NEWTS FOR **WEEKS**.

I COULD HAVE BEEN A BRITISH LION, BUT I COULDN'T STICK A BOOZY PARTY AN' TOUR EVERY 25 YEARS.

ALWAYS PREPARED TO HELP THOSE WHO CAN'T HELP **THEMSELVES HE IS.**

TRUE, HE'LL THUMP ANYONE WHO PROVOKES ONE OF **OWER** PLAYERS.

HIS ACTS OF KIND-NESS ARE **LEGENDARY**.

ALWAYS FIRST TO THE HOSPITAL TO VISIT THE PLAYER WOT HE **PUT** THERE HE IS **!**

CAN PLAY THE PIANO REAL WONDERFUL — AN' THERE'S NO STOPPIN' HIM **SINGIN'!**

AN' **STILL** NOT EVEN ON THE SHORT LIST FOR BBC WELSH SPORTS PERSONALITY. **DISGUSTIN'.**

'ANG ON PONTY BOY — 'ANG ON.

EE'S NOT EXACTLY A **SPORTSMAN** THOUGH ISSEE **?**

NO, BUT 'EE'S AN' 'ELL OF A **PERSONALITY** INNEE **?**

ISAMBARD KINGDOM LLEWELLYN 1960

Ponty an' Pop

GREN of the South Wales Echo

Now it's the English Rugby Union stealing our players not just the Northern League Clubs.

PROFESSIONAL RUGBY UNION HAS CERTAINLY MADE CHANGES IN OUR BIRTHRIGHT. THE RUGBY LOVING CITIZENS OF ROYAL ABERFLYARFF (VOTED PRETTIEST VILLAGE IN 1995 - SECOND WAS TREMORFA.) WERE BROUGHT UP TO HATE THE LIKES OF WIGAN, WIDNES AND ST HELENS BUT THEY ARE OK NOW. NOW WE HATE SARACENS AN' WEST HARTLEPOOL

WHERE IS THIS PLACE **SARACEN** THEN? I CAN'T FIND IT ON THE MAP.

WHERE EVER IT IS, THEY ARE **RICH**.

WELCOME TO
·ROYAL·
ABERFLYARFF
PLEASE DRIVE CAREFULLY (ON THE LEFT IF POSSIBLE)
TWINNED WITH THE WRU.

EXPANSIVE ST.

UK4   SAC

CARDIFF CITY: 'THE GLORY YEARS' NOW OUT IN PAPERBACK

I JUST DON'T UNDERSTAND HOW OWER STARS WILL **LEAVE** WALES - JUST FOR **MUNNEY**.

DON'T WALES MEAN **NOTHIN'** TO THEM? THEY'RE JUST MERCENARIES!

EXPANSIVE BRIDGE

HOW CAN YEW SWAP A DANK JANUARY DAY IN THE VALLEYS, FOR A QUICK **BUCK** IN SARACEN.

OR SWAP THE JOY OF LISTENIN' TO SEVENTEENTH CENTURY **BARDIC VERSE** ON RADIO WALES.

'OW CAN WEST 'ARTLEPOOL **COMPARE** WITH THAT - OR EVEN **ALL** OF 'ARTLEPOOL.

EXPANSIVE SQUARE

HUW·N·CRY   RENT-A MOB LTD

WHAT **COMPARES** WITH LISTENING TO DEWI AN' FRANK ON SUNDAY MORNING RADIO. AN' READING GRAHAM AN' SIMON IN THE **SPORTS** ECHO

THEN A COUPLE OF DECENT **WELSH** PINTS AT THE CLUB – HOME AGAIN FOR LUNCH AN' A KIP...

'TILL IT'S TIME FOR **ALAN** ON TELLY.

THEY HAVEN'T GOT **QUALITY** OF LIFE LIKE **THAT** IN ENGLAND!

SARACENS OFFER £50,000 FOR PROP PETER JONES – IF HE PROMISES TO STAY WITH BEDWAS RFC.

LOWER EXPANSIVE ROAD

HOW CAN PLACES LIKE SARACEN EVEN **THINK** THEY'RE RUGBY TOWNS.

– THEY'VE ONLY JUST LEARNED THE DIFFERENCE BETWEEN J.P.R AN' Q.P.R!

MERCENARIES OWER BOYS ARE – THEY DON'T PLAY THE GAME FOR THE SHEER **PLEASURE** OF GETTIN' THUMPED EVERY WEEK

UPPER EXPANSIVE ROAD

OR THE JOY OF KNOWIN' YEWER WELL-DIRECTED BUT SLY PUNCH HAS **SMASHED** HOME.

WELL THERE'S NO WAY AN ABERFLYARFF PLAYER WOULD SELL HIS SOUL TO **ENGLAND** AND **LEAVE** WALES!

WELSH THEY ARE, AN' IN WALES THEY'RE GONNA **STAY.**

'OW CAN YOU BE SO CONFIDENT PONTY?

When we're hungry there's nothing we enjoy more than a sweet chariot.

ENGLAND .V. WALES TWICKERS 3 FEB

EXPANSIVE AVENUE

I TOLD THEM I DID 'YOU SIGN FOR SARACEN OR WEST 'ARTLEPOOL OR **ANY** OF THEM RUBBISH ENGLISH CLUBS' I SAID...

'AN' I'LL GIVE THE **CHILD SUPPORT AGENCY** YEWER NEW ADDRESSES.

DUN, YEWER A **NARD** MAN PONTY!

Ye Golden Dap EXPANSIVE ALES

GREN 20.1.96

Ponty an' Pop

GREN of the South Wales Echo

Clubs are now offering huge playing fees. Will Royal Aberflyarff have to follow suit?

AS ANY FAN WILL KNOW, THE WHOLE WORLD OF RUGBY HAS BEEN SURPRISED TO LEARN THAT THE LATEST OF THE BIG SPENDING CLUBS, LIKE SARACENS IS ROYAL ABERFLYARFF.

ALL THE BIG NAMES COULD BE COMING.

DERWYN'S AGREED TERMS - £50,000 SIGNIN' ON AN' A THOUSAND A JUMP.

NEIL JENKS IS COMIN' TOO...

NEVER WHACK ANYONE WHO HAS A SOLICITOR. — Old Llanelli Proverb

I FEELS BAA-AAAD I DO.

ON CONDITION HE COULD BRING JUS' RENTALS AS WELL.

WELSH LANGUAGE SOCIETY DEMAND BILINGUAL ANABOLIC STERIODS FOR WEST WALES CLUBS. ☀ IN THE SPORTS ECHO

ENGLAND SADLY LOSE IN PARIS. THOUSANDS DELIGHTED IN WALES ECHO

WHERE'S ALL THE MUNNEY COMIN' FROM?

NO TROUBLE THERE - COULD BE MILLIONS IT COULD.

JONATHAN WOULD BE DELIGHTED TO JOIN US — SAID HE'D LOVE TO GET A REG'LAR GAME AGAIN.

JOCK STRAP RETREAD SHOP

WHILE U-WAIT

GREN 27·1·96

38

Ponty an' Pop

GREN

GREN of the South Wales Echo

It's another weekend away for the boys of Royal Aberflyarff RFC. This time it's to Twickenham.

IF THERE'S ONE THING THE RUGBY FANS OF LOVELY ROYAL ABERFLYARFF (Ignored by Wales Tourist Board yet again) LIKE, IT'S THE TWICKENHAM TRIP.

AS USUAL, THE PLANS FOR THE DAY ARE CHAOTIC, BUT EVEN SO ABERFLYARFF IS GOING.

I **LOVE** THE TWICKENHAM TRIP DON' YEW?

IVOR NURGE
ABERFLYARFF OFFICIAL FLASHER

TRADE ENQUIRIES WELCOME

SPECIAL RATES FOR GROUPS

CEC. PITT.

OUTSIDE LOOS LTD

WOT I WANTS TO KNOW IS...

8.2.96 GREN.

I DO, I DO. EVERYTIME I GO TO ENGLAND I FEEL LIKE A WELSH **MISSIONARY**. SPREADIN' THE GOOD WORD, AN' HELPIN' A STRUGGLING, EMERGIN' RUGBY NATION.

THERE'S NO DOUBT, THEY ARE **BEGINNING** TO PICK UP A BIT FROM US **REAL** RUGBY PEOPLE.

THEM ENGLISH FANS EVEN WANT TO GO TO **WATCH** THEIR SIDE AT TWICKENHAM NOW.

AYE, NOT LONG AGO YOU COULD BUY TWICKERS TICKETS, **FOUR** FOR A **QUID**.

IF THIS BLOKE JJ KNOWS EVERYTHING HOW IS IT...

Bleddyn - the club's security investment. Trained to go for the legs of any marauding league or union scout, also the legs of visiting backs with the line at their mercy.

CAN'T **GET** A TICKET NO-WHERE NOW.

IS THAT WHY SIXTY OF US ARE GOIN' UP ON A FIFTY SEATER, AN' NOT A **TICKET** BETWEEN US?

DON' WORRY, I **TOLD** YOU IT'LL BE ALL 'RIGHT-WELL **ALL** GET IN.

I GOT SOME OF THE BOYS DRESSED UP LIKE TOUCH-LINE **PHOTOGRAPHERS**...

SOME AS **STEWARDS**...

SOME AS **COPPERS**...

SOME AS **PRESS** BLOKES.

I BEEN ALL WEEK FORGIN' THE **PASSES**.

OH DON' BE DAFT MUN, THEY'LL **NEVER** GET THROUGH THE GATES DRESSED LIKE THAT WITH **FORGED** PASSES.

OH YES THEY WILL BUTTY BOY...

US TWELVE TURNSTILE OPERATORS WILL SEE TO THAT!

HE'S NOT

RUNNIN' THE WELSH SQUAD?

ABERFLYARFF OPRA 'OUSE

MANAGER RICK WRIGHT

★ TONIGHT ★
OWEN MONEY
BRYN YEMM
TOSCA
BRYN TERFEL
BINGO 8-9

ALL NEXT WEEK LORD CRICKHOWELL SINGS ZAHA HADID'S GREATEST HITS ★

TWICKERS SPECIAL

41

Ponty an' Pop

GREN of the South Wales Echo

The Welsh XV performed well at Twickenham. Narrowly losing to a much fanced England side.

PONTY, POP AND THE BOYS ARE BACK FROM TWICKERS, BACK TO LOVELY ROYAL ABER-FLYARFF. GATEWAY TO UTOPIA. ITS BEEN A HARD WEEK AS THEY'VE ALL BEEN CELEBRATING A GREAT WELSH DEFEAT. SOMETIMES IT CAN BE TOUGH BEING A WELSH RUGBY FAN.

WOT A PERFORMANCE EH - WE WOZ **BRILL**

THA'S IT INNIT- KEEP THE **SAME** SIDE I SAY.

WOT I SAY IS THIS

GREN. 10.2.96

GREAT PERFORMANCE! WE SHOULD 'AVE WON BY AT LEAST **TWELVE** POINTS.

MORE ID SAY- I BLAME THE **REF.**

ALL REFS SHOULD BE **WELSH**

BETHEL BAPTIST SUNDAY SERMON

IF WELSH RUGBY IS IN THE DOLDRUMS- WHY IS IT ENGLISH CLUBS WANT OUR PLAYERS?

- REV. BEN.E. DICTION. BE THERE!

OWER PACK WENT WELL - THEM SWING LOWERS COULDN'T **LIVE** WITH OWER BOYS.

I SEE THEY HAD TO DAMAGE DERWYN AN' JONATHAN TO **BALANCE** THINGS UP A BIT!

THA'S TREW!

SAM AN' ELLAS DINER

IF GOD HAD MEANT US TO HAVE A NATIONAL STADIUM IN BRIDGEND..

Ponty an' Pop

Royal Aberflyarff RFC are still desperately seeking a sponsor.

AFTER LAST WEEK'S INCREDIBLY EXCITING NEWS THAT THE ROYAL ABERFLYARFF R.F.C. TURNED DOWN A SPONSORSHIP DEAL FROM WELSH BREWERS (£10 A SEASON). THE RUGBY PRESS HAS PICKED UP THE STORY AND THE BREWERY NOW FEEL THEY SHOULD IMPROVE THEIR OFFER

SEEN THE **FOLLY** OF THEIR WAYS EH **?**

ROYAL ABERFLYARFF RFC REJECT BREWERY SPONSOR OFFER

ABERFLYARFF RFC INUNDATED BY AN OFFER.

LOCAL BREWERY BEG ABERFLYARFF RUGBY CLUB TO ACCEPT SPONSORSHIP

AYE, **WELSH BREWERS** HAVE NOW GOT TOGETHER WITH **BRAINS BREWERY**... AN' PUT TOGETHER AN **INTERESTIN'** PACKAGE.

WORTH **THOUSANDS** IT'LL BE.

THEY'VE SEEN US **PLAY**.

THEY'VE SEEN THE **SET** UP WOT WE GOT AT THE CLUB.

ABERFLYARFF SCENIC DRIVE.

AN' THEY KNOW THE RESPECT WOT WE GOT WITHIN THE **LOCAL COMMUNITY** TO SAY NOTHING OF THE RUGBY **WORLD**

IT'LL DO 'EM **GOOD** TO BE ASSOCIATED WITH **OWER** CLUB.

FO' SHEWER.

Bethel Baptist SUNDAY SERMON should Cardiff Athletic Club move to Cardiff bay?

Ponty an' Pop

GREN of the South Wales Echo

Isn't it just wonderful to hear Rugby League people complaining about us poaching their players...

THERE'S AN AIR OF JOY OVER LOVELY ROYAL ABERFLYARFF. ALL RUGBY LOVERS IN THE VILLAGE ARE HAPPY AND SMILING. AND AT PEACE WITH THE WORLD.

THE MOOD IS TYPIFIED BY PONTY, AND POP — EVEN BROMIDE LIL (Golden Haired Temptress at the Golden Dap) HAS NOTICED.

WOSSAMARRA WITH YEW TWO THEN. A BIT 'APPY ARENEW?

AYE ALL IS WONDERFUL IN OWER WORLD!

WHY WOSS-'APPENED?

YEW WOULDN'T UNDERSTAND LIL.

NO-YEW BEIN' A WOMAN LIKE!

ISS ALL TO DO WITH RUGBY SEE.

SCRUM FIVE BID £½M TO SCREEN JONATHAN'S OPERATION LIVE

ISS ALL ABOUT 'OW TRULY WONDERFUL IT IS FOR US UNION BLOKES TO SEE THEM LEAGUE PLAYERS COMIN' BACK INTO THE FOLD.

AFTER ALL THOSE YERS OF 'AVIN' TO PLAY THAT AWFUL GAME THAT THEY THINK IS RUGBY UP NORTH.

BACK TO US SEE TO PLAY REAL RUGBY.

CHICKEN CURRY ARFER NARF.

HAPPINESS IS A REF ON OUR SIDE

Y CYMRO
VINCENT KANE TO BECOME CHAIRMAN OF WELSH LANGUAGE SOCIETY

Dai the Dap - ex famed winger of Llanelli, Swansea, Cardiff & Pontypridd who is now playing in the twilight of his career, where he has been for the last twenty-two seasons on the right wing for Royal Aberflyarff RFC.

His career almost came to an untimely end at Swansea when his dap blew out doing sixty in a Barbarian game when he'd left Rory Underwood for dead.

Ponty an' Pop

GREN of the South Wales Echo

Stories of mega-rich union clubs casting their nets in Wales abound...

49

It seems that these days our wonderful game is all about money, money and even more money...

LOVELY ROYAL ABERFLYARFF IS AWASH THIS WEEK, WITH STRANGE PEOPLE. WHO SPEAK IN A TONGUE NOT EASILY UNDERSTOOD (Like they do in Llanelli) THEY WEAR CHECK SKIRTS, PLAY BAGPIPES (which is claimed by some to be a 'musical instrument') AS THEY SING A LOT ABOUT A SCOTTISH BREWERY (Flowers of Scotland)

IT'S **GREAT** TO HAVE THE JOCKS HERE AGAIN EH?

I ONLY HOPE AS HOW THEY HAVEN'T BEEN PUT OFF ABOUT HOW MUCH OWER WELSH TEAM CAN **EARN.**

TELL ME. **OWER** BOYS AT THE RUGBY CLUB ARE NEGOTIATING WITH ME OVER **THEIR** TERMS.

WELL ACCORDIN' TO THE **ECHO** - THE TRUMPET OF TRUTH - THE WELSH SQUAD HAVE REACHED AGREEMENT WITH THE WRU.

WOS THE WRU DONE?

FIRST OWER BOYS 'AVE AGREED TO A $5,000 **RETAINER.**

OH IM NOT SURE **THAT'S** A GOOD MOVE.

YE GOLDEN DAP
BAR FOOD
PORRIDGE
xxx
HAGGIS +CHIPS
xxx
HAGGIS BUTTY
xxx

EDINBURGH SPEEKED HERE.
CROESO JOCK INNIT

WOT I SAY IS...

GREN. 17-2-96

ABERFLYARFF AND WALES WELCOMES ALL SCOTS FANS

THIS SWANSEA CITY SOCCER MANAGER—

Ponty an' Pop

GREN of the South Wales Echo

Rugby friendships last forever - or so it is believed.

THE GREAT THING ABOUT RUGBY IS ITS CAMERADERIE. PLAYERS OF YESTERDAY ARE NEVER FORGOTTEN.
SO TOO, AT ROYAL ABERFLYARFF RFC (NO BUNGS) LTD, WHERE PONTY AND POP REMEMBER ONE OF THE CLUBS TRUE GREATS.

REMEMBER HIM? **LATE TACKLE LLOYD** - WHAT A PLAYER!

WOT HE'S DONE FOR THIS CLUB! WOT A **NERO** HE WAS.

ABERFLYARFF HALL OF FAME

KING JROW.

LATE TACKLE LLOYD

MELVYN NUTSTRAMPLER

TREMBLIN' MEG

DON'T MOVE THE STADIUM

STILL GOT THE CLUB RECORD SEE.

SENT OFF MORE TIMES THAN **ANYONE** ELSE,

HE WAS BILINGUAL IN FOUL LANGUAGE TOO! **GREAT** ASSET HE WOZ.

BARRY'S HAND PRINT

OLD NORTH ENC TICKET

MERLE'S TEETH

ERICA ROE

POOR OLD NIGEL WALKER, HE'S GOT WHAT THEY CALL HOKEY-COKEY SHOULDER.

AN' FOR THREE CONSECUTIVE SEASONS HE HE WON THE **MUCH** COVETED GBH-OF-THE SEASON-AWARD.

AN' HE WAS ON THE BLACK LIST OF **EVERY** HOTELLIER IN DEVON HE WAS.

THE **ONLY** PLAYER THAT DEAN RICHARDS IS TERRIFIED OF.

ABERFLYARFF RFC (CADW INTERESTED 1980)

IT'S 'IN-OUT, IN-OUT SHAKE IT ALL ABOUT...

GREN 25·2·95

Ronald the Ref
Very sad case is Ronald, he played for Royal Aberflyarff for nearly nineteen glorious years before his pace went and his eyesight failed and due to age he began to forget the rules.
It will come as no surprise to Rugby lovers everywhere that Ronald did the usual thing.
Yes, he became a ref.

Ponty an' Pop

GREN of the South Wales Echo

Video evidence seems to have become very popular with some clubs whose players have been rather naughty.

YET AGAIN SHAME WAS HEAPED UPON THE PROUD VILLAGE OF LOVELY ROYAL ABER-FLYARFF, AFTER ARNOLD NUTSTRAMPLER CLUB CAPTAIN AND TIGHTHEAD PROVOKER, WAS SUSPENDED BY THE WRU.

NOBODY SAW THE INCIDENT AT THE TIME - BUT THE W.R.U **BANNED** ARNOLD ANYWAY AFTER STUDYING VIDEO EVIDENCE.

WOT 'APPENED SEE WOZ WE WOZ PLAYIN' DIRTY NASTY LLANFAIRFILTHI - ALWAYS A VERY HIGHLY **COMMITTED** GAME IT IS.

A RUCK BROKE UP AN' OUT OF IT CAME THEIR BLINDSIDE STIFF ARMER - WITHOUT NO **YERS** !

SOME ONE HAD **BITTEN** BOTH YERS RIGHT OFF !

WE ASKED HIM 'WHO BIT YEWER YERS OFF?' BUT HE COULDN'T HEAR US SEE.

CARDIFF RFC CURRENT OUTSIDE HALVES ANNUAL DINNER TONIGHT

WHO IS THRUSH?

WOTS GOT SIXTEEN LEGS - IS VERY HAIRY, AN...

Ponty an' Pop

Whatever happens in the country you can bet it will happen sooner or later in Royal Aberflyarff.

IT'S BEEN A DEPRESSING WEEK IN LOVELY ROYAL ABERFLYARFF (WHERE MEN ARE MEN, AND WE'RE NOT TOO SHRE ABOUT SOME OF THE WOMEN.) AS VILLAGERS DISCUSS THE LATEST SHAME BROUGHT ON THE VILLAGE BY YET ANOTHER OF ITS RUGBY PLAYERS.

'AVE YEW YEARD LIL? DENZIL THE DRUIP 'AVE BEEN **ARRESTED** BY THE POLICE!

NOT DENZIL THE DRUID OWER OPENSIDE **MISSILE**.

SOYA + CHIPS
SOYA BUTTIES
SOYA SALAD
SOYA PUDDING

BAR

BORN TO RUCK

GREN 30.3.96

AYE THA'S HIM WOT A **GREAT** PLAYER

WE WOZ PLAYIN' THE PORTH BRANCH OF THE WILL CARLING APPRECIATION SOCIETY.

WOT A **GAME**

YEW KNOW WOT THAT LOT ARE LIKE – ALL POCKETS IN THEIR SHORTS AN' THINK THEY **INVENTED** EXPANSIVE.

AN' **WHO** DID THEY HAVE PLAYIN' AT *OUTSIDE ARFF THAT DAY? – UNDER AN ASSUMED NAME ... **JONATHAN DAVIES**.

A.N. OTHER EH?

NO, **WILL CARLING**.

THOSE PLAYERS WISHING TO JOIN HARLEQUINS OR OTHER HEATHEN CLUBS CAN'T GO ON THE WRU OUTING –SO THERE!

BY ORDER WRU.

* OR STEAND ORFF IF YOU'RE FROM COWBRIDGE

Ponty an' Pop

GREN of the South Wales Echo

Easter means Barbarians to every Rugby loving Welshman.

Cyclops Llewellyn
In every club there has to be a Llanelli fan - its compulsory (WRU Minute 107-3a).
Well Cyclops is ours . You can always tell a Llanelli fan, they begin every sentence with - "think he's good? I tell you at Llanelli we got a boy in our youth team...."